GOOD
LUCK
GOLD
& more

ADDITIONAL SELECTED TITLES
BY JANET WONG

Poetry Collections
A Suitcase of Seaweed & MORE
Behind the Wheel: Poems about Driving
Knock on Wood: Poems about Superstitions
The Rainbow Hand: Poems about Mothers and Children
TWIST: Yoga Poems

Picture Books
Alex and the Wednesday Chess Club
Apple Pie 4th of July
Homegrown House
This Next New Year
   (English-only; Chinese-English Edition; Korean-English Edition)

Chapter Books / Novels in Verse
Me and Rolly Maloo
Minn and Jake
Minn and Jake's Almost Terrible Summer

Books on Writing
Before It Wriggles Away
You Have to Write

The Poetry Friday Power Book Series (with Sylvia Vardell)
HERE WE GO: A Poetry Friday Power Book
PET CRAZY: A Poetry Friday Power Book
YOU JUST WAIT: A Poetry Friday Power Book

Other Poetry Anthologies (with Sylvia Vardell)
GREAT Morning! Poems for School Leaders to Read Aloud
HOP TO IT: Poems to Get You Moving
The Poetry Friday Anthology for Celebrations
The Poetry Friday Anthology for Science
The Poetry of Science

GOOD
LUCK
GOLD

& more

janet wong

YUZU

AN IMPRINT OF POMELO BOOKS

To Glenn

100% of the profits from this book will be donated
to charities that #StopAsianHate and provide bystander training

Y U Z U
An imprint of Pomelo Books
4580 Province Line Road
Princeton, NJ 08540
www.PomeloBooks.com
info@PomeloBooks.com

Copyright © 1994, © 2021 by Janet S. Wong.
All rights reserved.
Library of Congress Cataloging-in-Publication Data is available.
ISBN 978-1-937057-76-3

Please visit:
www.JanetWong.com
www.PomeloBooks.com

CONTENTS

ABOUT THIS BOOK

My first book, *Good Luck Gold and Other Poems,* was published in 1994 by Margaret K. McElderry Books, part of Macmillan. That original collection contained 42 poems. When the book went out of print—yes, books "die"—I got the rights back and brought it back to life. I added an Author's Note and a new cover, but other than that, it was the same as the original book.

This book is not just another new version; it's a whole new book, with more than double the content. For some of the poems, I decided to write about the "story behind the story." For other poems, I decided to write about the "story *after* the story," things I've been wondering about recently that are connected with the poem (in my brain). Either way, in the paragraphs and questions on the right-hand pages, you'll hopefully find something new to think about. And to talk about. And to write about, too. I would love it if this book helped you write a book of your own.

I was going to rearrange the poems and put them into themed sections, such as poems about Chinatown, poems about racism, poems about food, poems about identity, and poems about "just growing up." But these themes are layered and linked together like skin and muscle and bone.

It often feels complicated and confusing when we talk about race, culture, and identity. That's OK. Let's try.

Do you have any old pieces of writing
where you can write "the story after the story"?
What things have you been wondering about recently?

GOOD LUCK GOLD

When I was a baby
one month old,
my grandparents gave me
good luck gold:
a golden ring
so soft it bends,
a golden necklace
hooked at the ends,
a golden bracelet
with coins that say
I will be rich
and happy someday.

I wish that gold
would work
real soon.
I need my luck
this afternoon.

I was born in Los Angeles. My Chinese grandparents threw a "red egg and ginger" party for me at a restaurant in L.A.'s Chinatown. This is where I was given the good luck gold that you can see on the cover of this book.

I'm pretty sure that someone—my grandfather?—told me that I was one month old when I was given those tiny pieces of jewelry. But I read online that it has become trendy for all kinds of people (not just Chinese people) to have red egg and ginger parties for *100-day-old* babies. I was puzzled and started wondering how old I really was when I got my good luck gold jewelry. My father didn't remember, but decided I was "probably 100 days old." Maybe I should revise this poem to read: "When I was a baby / 100 days old / my grandparents gave me / good luck gold."

Some families throw a baby shower when a mother is still pregnant, or they celebrate the birth right after returning from the hospital. But centuries ago, when many babies died in their first few weeks of life, superstitious people kept quiet about their newborn babies to avoid the attention of the gods. They even gave them ugly nicknames. What god would want to kidnap a child called "Stinky"?

I asked a group of Chinese immigrants (middle school students) in New York if they had been given good luck gold. One of them said, "I've heard about it. That's some old-fashioned custom, right?"

How are babies celebrated
in the culture(s) of your heritage?
Can you ask someone about it?

MY BIRD DAY

When my grandfather says birthday
in his Chinese accent,
it sounds like "bird day,"
which is closer to truth—
for us, anyway.

At my birthday parties
we never have
paper streamers,
piñatas in trees,
balloons taped up
on the wall.
We decorate with platters
of peking duck,
soy sauce chicken and squab
in lettuce cups.
Food is all
that matters.

Other Chinese families
might do things
differently,
but my grandfather,
whose name is Duck,
thinks it's good
luck to make
a bird day
special.

When I was a teen, my family went to a party where there were about two dozen people. I remember loving every single thing there: music, dancing, paper decorations, flowers, balloons—and lots of potato chips. Everyone was talking loudly and laughing. I was so happy. I had never been to anything like it.

When we got in the car, my mother complained. "*That* was a party? Where was the food? Chips? Just chips! That was *not* a party." Right then all the balloons of joy inside of me popped, one by one by one.

Years later, when my parents owned a mini-mart in a small town in Oregon, they let me buy things for the store. Things to sell and also just things that would make the place look bright and happy. I spent hours ordering balloons. Each time I visited the store, I would fill a few balloons and tie them to the rack of potato chips at the register, so they could grab a balloon and a big bag of chips—and make any regular day feel like a party.

Can you remember a party that you loved?
If you could plan a small surprise party for a friend,
what would you do to make it special?

Lessons

Melissa has lessons—
judo, ballet—
after school
and Saturdays.
Steven paints
at the art museum.
June is learning
to speak Korean.
       I stay home
doing chores.

I cook meals
for my brother
and me,
make the beds
with fresh sheets,
do the dishes
from the day
before,
sweep and mop
the hardwood floor.
       Still I dream,
when I'm alone,
of lessons
I'll take
when I am grown.

When I was little, my father often took me to Griffith Park, a 20-minute drive from our apartment, where I rode ponies around and around in a small ring. There were usually two or three dozen kids there. We were divided into groups: walk, trot, and canter. I only rode in the canter group a couple of times.

We went there until I was seven, when we moved to Northern California. At my new school I knew a girl who took riding lessons. She told me I could take lessons, too. But we had just barely enough money for food and house payments. Still, I spent hours bent over the H volume of the encyclopedia, learning about different horse breeds so I would know which kind of horse to buy, in case we ever got rich.

When I was a freshman at college, I finally did get to take horseback riding lessons. UCLA had a special program where you wait all day in a long line for the chance to sign up for swimming lessons, or golf lessons, or riding lessons. I was the best student in the riding class, completely comfortable on my horse, until we had to jump. *Oof! Ouch! Ugh!* I fell to the left, fell to the right, and even fell over the head of my horse. I gritted my teeth whenever we approached a bar.

The last time I rode a horse (three years ago on lava fields in Iceland), we walked almost the whole way—but in my mind, we were flying.

What would you like to learn?
What lessons do you wish you could take?
Can you start teaching yourself with books or videos?

ALL MIXED UP

What does *multicultural* mean?

Stuck in the middle
in between
all kinds of food
and clothes
and talk?
Listening to bamboo flutes
play rock?
Turning tortillas
over the stove,
burning the tips
of chopsticks?

Why does my teacher love that word?
Is it something she ate—
or something she heard?
Loud drums
beating in the park?
Does she call me
multicultural
because my skin is
dark?

The words we use to talk about "multicultural" things keep changing. When I was a kid, people asked me about "Oriental" customs. In high school, one of my teachers told me that his Chinese friends used the term "Asian" or "Asian American." It sounded odd to me when I started using those words, but I got used to it. A lot of people now use "AAPI" (Asian American Pacific Islander). By the time you're reading this, there might be a new name.

There are some customs that are shared by many Asian people, such as the use of chopsticks, but be careful: there are differences even in something as small as chopsticks. Traditional Chinese chopsticks are usually made of bamboo, with blunt round tips. Traditional Korean chopsticks are usually made of metal, and thin and flat. And yet today, most people rarely use traditional chopsticks; we use (and reuse) disposable bamboo or wooden chopsticks. Disposable chopsticks are especially useful when you're cooking. You don't have to worry if you burn the tips. If they start looking bad, then you can stick them in the soil of a potted plant to give your plant something to lean on.

The way we live with culture nowadays is like that. When you get culture with your restaurant takeout, you can throw it away. Or you can use it and reuse it, and find some smart way for it to help things grow.

How many different cultures
have you grown up with?
Do you do anything that might be a mix of cultures?

SPEAK UP

You're Korean, aren't you?

> *Yes.*

Why don't you speak
Korean?

> *Just don't, I guess.*

Say something Korean.

> *I don't speak it.*
> *I can't.*

C'mon. Say something.

> Halmoni. *Grandmother.*
> Haraboji. *Grandfather.*
> Imo. *Aunt.*

Say some other stuff.
Sounds funny.
Sounds strange.

> *Hey, let's listen to you*
> *for a change.*

Listen to me?

> *Say some foreign words.*

But I'm American,
can't you see?

> *Your family came from*
> *somewhere else.*
> *Sometime.*

But I was born here.

> *So was I.*

My father came to the United States from China when he was 12 years old. My parents met when my father was a soldier with the U.S. Army in Korea. After they married, they lived in Los Angeles, where I was born. My father didn't speak much Korean and my mother didn't speak any Chinese. We spoke to each other in English.

By the time I was five years old, some kids—at my school, in the park, and even when we were shopping in the supermarket—had made fun of me for being Asian. It didn't happen all the time, but it hurt. They would make "Chinese-sounding" noises and pull at their eyes. They would tell me to say some words in Korean or Chinese, and then they would mock those words. No one ever asked my white friends to speak German or Italian or French.

In this poem I sound like I'm saying that I don't want to speak Korean, but the opposite is the truth. I wish I spoke Korean, my mother's native language. I wish I spoke Chinese, my father's native language. I wish all of that—now. But when I was a child, I thought that learning Chinese or Korean would give the bullies more to tease me about. So I decided that I wouldn't learn those languages. I let bullies steal my family languages from me.

What are the languages of your heritage?
Would you like to learn them—or any other languages?

LUCKY

Used to be
our back-fence neighbor
old John Lee
would read
to me.
That was way back when
before he couldn't
talk and couldn't see,
before he fell and moved
into the nursing home
behind my school.
Lucky that
he taught me well;
now I can read
to old John Lee.

When you visit people in nursing homes or hospitals, it's hard to sit there doing nothing. It's tricky to find something to say when you are with people who are too sick to talk. You could spend the whole time looking at your phone, but then what's the point of visiting?

The next time you find yourself in a situation like this, maybe you can sit there and read aloud to them—even if they cannot say anything in response.

I did that one day; I read to my friend who was in a coma in the hospital. Everyone thought she was going to die that week. We thought she wasn't hearing anything. But when she came back to life and I saw her a month later, she talked to me about what I had read to her that day. She had been listening. I wonder if hearing me read might've helped her get better? I want to think that it did.

The next time you feel sad, the next time you feel sick and alone, pick up a book. Read aloud to yourself. Let the book be your medicine.

What poems or picture books or stories do you love?
If you were in the hospital and could not speak,
what could we read to help you feel happy?

CHINATOWN

Why do we go to Chinatown?
To eat and shop and look around
at all the different Chinese faces
seldom seen in other places.

What do I like best down there?
The crispy, thick, salty air
spilling out the restaurant doors—
and New Year's firecracker wars.

I was probably 9 or 10 years old when I first heard some kids say that Chinese people all look alike. How could they think that? I knew for a fact that Chinese people could look very different from one another; anyone could go to Chinatown and see a hundred very different-looking people. After all, there are more than 50 ethnic groups in China, identified by their history, language, religion, customs, clothing, and even physical appearance.

One great place to see this at a glance—if you're not near a Chinatown—is the opening ceremony of the Olympics. A Chinese basketball player might be tall, with a square head, a long pointed nose, full lips, and bushy eyebrows; while a Chinese gymnast might look very different, short and small-boned, with a triangle-shaped head, a button nose, thin lips, and very round eyes.

There won't be anything close to the diversity you'll see in the teams representing the United States or Canada or Australia or the United Kingdom. But the Chinese team members won't all look alike, either.

What are the physical traits that define you?
Now think: what really defines who you are?
How much of you can we see?

WAITING AT THE RAILROAD CAFÉ

All the white kids are eating.
"Let's go, Dad," I say.
"Let's get out of this place."
But Dad doesn't move.
He's going to prove
the Asian race
is equal. We stay
and take our silent beating.

He folds his arms
across his chest
glaring at the waitresses who
pass by like cattle
ready for a western battle.
They will not look, they refuse to
surrender even to my best
wishing on bracelet charms.

"Consider this part of your education,"
Dad says. I wonder how long
we'll be ignored, like hungry ghosts
of Chinese men who laid this track,
never making their journeys back
but leaving milestones and signposts
to follow. "Why do they treat us so wrong?"
I wonder. "Don't they know we're on
vacation?"

A drunk shouts at us and
gets louder and redder
in the face
when we pay
him no mind. I say
"Let's get out of this place.
We're not equal. We're better,"
as I pull Dad by the hand.

I was traveling from California to Yellowstone with my father. We stopped into a small diner near the railroad tracks in a tiny town. There were about a dozen people sitting down, but there were still plenty of empty tables. We stood near the register and waited to be seated. And waited. And waited, then seated ourselves at a table near the door.

The waitresses ignored us. We weren't given menus, water, smiles—nothing. We sat as if we were invisible, my father growing madder by the minute. I think this was a case of racism, but I'm not 100% sure. Maybe they saw our California license plate and ignored us because they hated people from California.

During the civil rights struggles of the 1960s, when Black activists challenged racist segregation laws and practices in restaurants, they often were ignored, as if they were invisible. That was considered a victory because a more common outcome was to be beaten or thrown out on the street. You can read about some of these heroes in books, but there are thousands of everyday heroes we don't know for each one in the news. Chances are, you know an everyday hero. There might be a relative of yours who has stood up to racism with peaceful protest. Ask your family. Listen. Put those stories down on paper. Keep their stories alive.

Have you ever been the victim of racism—
or witnessed a racist act?
What did you do?

BOUND FEET

Smoothing her fingers,
PoPo shows how, back in China, long ago
they used to roll young girls' feet,
soaked in salt for softer bones,
rolled and rolled and rolled and tied
in packages of tender meat.

Hearing that, I like my feet.

For centuries in China, young girls had their feet bound at age five or six, if they were rich. If they were poor but exceptionally beautiful—and not needed for work in the fields—then their feet might be bound, too. This would give them a chance at marrying rich. Most marriages were arranged by the time a girl was 15 or 16 years old. Rich boys would marry rich girls, and poor girls would marry poor boys—unless the poor girl was exceptionally beautiful and had been prepared to fit into high society by having her feet bound as a child.

Rich Chinese girls were told that their small, bound feet showed that they were members of the upper class. Some girls managed to handle the pain of bound feet well enough to walk and even perform acrobatic dances, but most women with bound feet experienced such tremendous pain that they spent all of their time seated or in bed.

I have read about several different foot-binding methods, and all of them sound cruel and painful. My grandmother told me that her grandmother's feet were soaked in salt water for a day, and then the bones were broken, and the feet were rolled and tied into fist-shaped balls. My grandmother first talked to me about this at the end of a long day of shopping, when I was pestering her because I wanted a fancy but clearly uncomfortable pair of high-heeled shoes. After hearing her story, I changed my mind and decided that my wide sneakers were just fine.

*What are some odd things that people have done
at different times in history to make themselves "beautiful"?
What are some uncomfortable things that we do to "look good"?*

FAMILY STYLE

Like hungry sea gulls,
chopsticks fight, trying to snatch
the best piece of fish.

In some of the top restaurants all over the world today, clever chefs are finding ways to reduce the amount of food they waste. Traditional Chinese chefs have been thinking this way for centuries. All parts of an animal are used. Meat and vegetables are cut into small pieces in the kitchen and served "family style." Instead of each person having a set portion placed on their plate, the platters are put in the middle of the table. Everyone takes only what they want to eat. I grew up eating family style almost every night, even when we were eating pasta or tacos.

When you take food from the common dishes on the table, you need to use the serving chopsticks or spoon, or at least the clean end of your chopsticks—not the end that has gone into your mouth already. And when you reach in, you should do it politely, not like a bunch of hungry seagulls.

At least this is how you *should* do it. When everyone at the table is starving, watch the feathers fly!

Do you ever eat "family style" at home?
What do you prefer: eating family style,
or having a pre-set amount of food served on your own plate?

ANYWHERE

If you could live anywhere
in the world,
where would you live?

Know what I heard?

I heard there's a place
in the mountains
somewhere
where fun is free
and people play fair.
If you feel bad,
neighbors care.

The air smells green,
crisp and clean.
Water's fresh
from the spring.
You can pick berries
to picnic on
near waterfalls
and streams.

When school's out
I'm going there.
Want to come?

Come.

There's plenty
to share.

My grandfather moved to the United States from China in the 1920s and worked on farms in California. After the stock market crashed in 1929, this country was launched into a period of poverty called the Depression. Jobs were scarce. My grandfather had no money saved because he had sent it all to China to help his family. How could he live without savings or a job?

There were bread lines in the United States during the Depression, but he didn't stand in the bread lines; a Chinese man would not have been given any government aid. So he and his buddies lived homeless in the wilderness. They camped in makeshift tents. They spent their days hunting, fishing, and foraging—living off the land. He did this for a couple of years until he decided to return to China to get married and start a family of his own.

When I was a child and saw homeless people pushing their belongings in grocery carts or living in cardboard boxes, I often wondered why they didn't move up to the mountains to hunt and camp. I now understand that things are often complicated for a homeless person; I understand that there are often problems that I cannot see. Still, I love the idea of escaping to a quiet place in nature. It makes me happier every time I hike in the woods or sit near a stream. You too?

What kind of places do you love most:
busy city streets, quiet parks, beaches, woods—
or something else?

CHOW TIME

In another life I am sure
I was a dog.
Especially
on a hot morning
when I find myself
lying
in bed
on my side,
legs limp,
stretched out
ninety degrees
in the lamp
of my window,
so doggone
tired
nothing
could make me move
except
the smell
of
food.

I love the idea of reincarnation, but I don't really believe in it, except that sometimes I wonder if my dog had a past life as a person. He acts like some people I have known.

People often talk about how, in another life, they were famous: army generals, presidents, kings and queens. You don't often hear someone say that in another life they were a farmer or a cook or a nurse. And usually they talk about another human life—they were some type of human, before; they were never ants or rats or bacteria.

People throughout the world hold many different beliefs about what happens before or after our lives on this earth. Some people even believe that it's possible to live multiple lives at the same time. They think we can walk through portals into different parallel universes. That must be what is happening to me when all of a sudden my mind goes blank and I wonder, "What was I saying?"

If you were something or someone else in another life,
what might you have been?
Who or what would you like to have been?

LOSING FACE

Finally Mother is proud
of something
I have done.
"My girl won
the art contest,"
she tells the world,
smiling so big
and laughing so loud
her gold tooth
shows.

I am the only one
who knows
how I drew so well,
erasing the perfect lines
I traced,
drawing worse ones
on purpose
in their place.
I feel awful.
I want to tell.

But I don't want to lose
Mother's glowing
proud face.

When I was a young child, I loved to draw. My father bought me a "how to draw" book when I was in fourth grade and I tried drawing the animals in the book, but never managed to get things right. A beak or a foot or a tail was always a little off. I didn't understand that the best artists often don't care if things in their art look real.

In sixth grade, everyone at our school was invited to submit a drawing for an art contest. I tried to draw one of the birds that I saw in my book. I used up a whole pad of expensive paper, but my bird never turned out the way I wanted. So finally I used thin paper to trace it. Then I rubbed the traced lines onto a thick piece of fancy paper. (This actually is a technique that some professional artists use, but it felt like cheating to me.) When I sat back to admire my work, it looked too perfect, so I erased some of the lines and drew other wobbly lines instead. When my best friend saw it, she said, "You traced." I was angry and ashamed. I should've just admitted the truth, but I lied. I'm not sure what was worse, the cheating or lying.

I won the contest. My prize: a large backpack with an aluminum frame built for a person six feet tall. I am not even five feet tall. I gave that backpack to Goodwill.

Have you ever done something that made you ashamed?
Have you ever received praise that you didn't deserve?

Rich

I'd rather my mother be rich
than me—
I don't need a lot
of things.
But I know my mother
wants a warm new coat
and a real gold chain
(the fake one broke)
and a house
of our own
with a yard
and a pool.
I wish she could have it.
I'll work after school
when I'm old enough—
as soon as I can.
I'm going to be
my mother's
helping hand.

My mother grew up extremely poor. Sometimes the only thing her family had for dinner was one bowl of rice, one small bowl for five people to share, each one eating just a few mouthfuls.

We were not poor, but I remember feeling that we were, mainly because we could not afford to buy all the things that my mother wanted to eat. For most of her life she weighed less than ninety pounds, but she could eat more than anyone I know. When we had a little extra money, she would stuff our refrigerator with food that was on sale. She would seem a little happier—at least until the refrigerator grew empty again.

One of the things she used to half-joke about was wanting to be rich enough to buy a fur coat. We lived in California and it was only cold enough to need a heavy coat about two weeks out of the year, but I remember wishing, often, that we could become rich enough to buy her the coat she wanted. My father finally bought a fur coat for her when she was sixty years old. I saw her wear it a handful of times, including on some days when it was just "sweater weather." She would be standing outside in the church parking lot, wearing the fur coat, her face blushing hot pink.

If you suddenly won some unexpected money,
would you buy something or save it?
How could money change your life?

BONSAI

Why would
anyone want
to turn a strong young tree
into something so twisted, rough
and old?

My father's high school friends at L.A. High were mainly Japanese Americans with a strong cultural upbringing, and so my father learned a lot about Japanese culture when he was a teen. When I was in elementary school, we spent many weekends in the "J town" or Little Tokyo section of Los Angeles. I grew up knowing as much about Japanese culture as I knew about Chinese and Korean culture. We had Chinese chopsticks, Korean chopsticks, and shiny lacquered Japanese chopsticks, too. We had blue and white Japanese dishes, Japanese vases, and a large Japanese platter with a bonsai tree sitting in it.

The bonsai trees in stores in Little Tokyo looked so beautiful, so rugged and strong despite being so tiny. Ours at home never looked as good. Bonsai trees are not easy plants. If you are not careful, it takes just a few weeks to kill a tree that is twenty years old.

One day, after I had killed yet another bonsai—probably by giving it too much water—I felt both sad and angry. I wondered why we would want to take care of such fussy little trees. I wrote this poem remembering that day.

Do you have a favorite plant in your house or garden?
Have you ever had a houseplant that died?
How did it make you feel?

The Visit

Just in case
I miss you
come morning—

Just in case
you sneak
out the door
before
I wake—

Remember
to give me
a kiss
on my forehead—

Remember the rest
of your birthday
cake—

Remember when we
all lived
together?

Remember—
I love you.

Just in case.

My father traveled a lot for work. Sometimes he was gone for more than a month; and when he returned, it was sometimes just for a weekend. One time when he came back, he seemed different. His face was thinner or his hair was much longer, or he just acted really tired and said strange things. I remember thinking he was an imposter. I was sure that my real father had been kidnapped.

This was not such a crazy thing to believe because I had two pets who mysteriously disappeared before I was five years old: a cat who supposedly jumped out of the car window on the freeway, and a pup who supposedly ran away when my mother and I went to Korea to visit my grandparents. If our pets could vanish, my father could too, right? In a way, my father did vanish when I was 34 years old. After 37 years of marriage, my parents divorced. Even though I was not a child any longer, I was still their child—and all of a sudden my world was turned upside down.

Everything in this world was turned upside down in 2020 at the start of the pandemic. But just remember: as topsy-turvy as things may seem, there is always someone who cares, someone who will listen, someone who wants to help. Make a list of the people you can count on—your family, your friends and their families, your teachers, your librarians, your neighbors, your old babysitters. We will be there for you, just in case.

What do you worry about?
What can you tell your worrying self?
Is there anyone who needs your help?

Bombs Bursting in Air

At the Dodgers game
last Saturday
we sat behind a row
of big rowdy guys
downing beers
and clowning around,
spitting split peanut shells
in the air.
        When it came time
for the national anthem,
and the giant screen
deep in center field
showed the singer's face—
an Asian face—
those guys spit "Jap!"
and laughed
all the way through.
        The singer's strong
voice drowned them out,
though, until the end,
when he bowed his head
and the loud clapping
of the crowd
filled the stadium.
        He waved
and smiled my way.
I waved back,
hot dog in hand,
relish spilling out, proud
until I heard
"Bet that's all
the American he knows,"
and felt a shell
land on my arm.

During the summer of 2021, right before the Home Run Derby and All-Star Game, a sports commentator suggested that Shohei Ohtani was a poor representative for Major League Baseball since he uses an interpreter with the media. Shohei is studying English and people have heard him speaking English with his teammates during games, but he prefers to handle interviews in his native language, Japanese.

Baseball fans quickly defended Shohei by pointing to comparisons between him and Babe Ruth; the commentator was widely denounced as a racist buffoon. Other baseball analysts commented that several of the best young baseball stars, such as Ronald Acuña, Jr. and Vladimir Guerrero, Jr., use interpreters and prefer their home language of Spanish even though they can speak in English.

Less than one month later, Team USA won the silver medal in Men's Baseball at the Tokyo Olympics. Who won the gold medal? The Japanese team.

How many great baseball players can you name?
How many of them were born or raised
in a country other than the U.S.?

MATH

"Asians are supposed to be good at math."
Mr. Chao can't figure me out.
"Asians are quiet. Asians like numbers."
Me, I like to shout.

In ninth grade, I sat next to two friends who allowed me to take some "shortcuts" in our algebra class. I got good grades but I didn't really learn the math. Because of those high grades, I was put in an advanced math program in tenth grade where, without the help of my friends, I did very poorly.

My Algebra 2 teacher was puzzled. I was in his class only because I'd done well in Algebra 1. How could I suddenly be so stupid?

Mr. Lau decided that I must have become too busy with friends or afterschool clubs. He pulled me aside to scold me. He said, "I don't understand: Asians are supposed to be good at math!"

I wrote this poem three years after my husband and I moved into our house—a house which happened to be on the same street where Mr. Lau lived. Mr. Lau was a good teacher and a kind man, but every time I saw him in his yard, I thought of that conversation—and how rotten it made me feel, like I was a bad Asian. The "model minority" myth that Asians should excel in school (especially in math) can put a lot of pressure on a "regular" Asian kid.

The funny thing: I was rotten at algebra, but great at geometry in 11th grade. So if you think you're bad at math, maybe you just haven't found "your kind" of math yet!

Has anyone ever stereotyped you?
What assumptions did they make that were wrong?
What things are you good at—that don't fit a stereotype?

NOISE

Ching chong Chinaman

Those kids over there
are laughing at me.
    My hair.
    My nose.
    My skin.
I hear the noise.
Ching chong
I won't let it in.

They're pulling their lids
up, down and out
to the side,
making wide eyes slit thin,
faking being
some kind of Chinese
I've never seen,
chanting

Ching chong ching chong
Open your eyes
Open your eyes, Chinese

It's only noise.
Ching chong
I won't let it in.
I won't let it in.

I promise myself

I won't let them
win.

Before I wrote this poem, I attended an all-day "Multicultural Teach-In" at a public television station where writers, educators, and people who worked in the entertainment industry gathered to brainstorm how we could do better at honoring inclusion and promoting social justice. A day care center director talked about an Asian child at her school who was taunted by the other children. They would chase him around the playground shouting, "Ching chong: open your eyes! Open your eyes, Chinese!" The director said that she punished the children, but nothing worked. The taunting continued.

When I saw my mother a few weeks later, I said, "Can you believe that the children are so mean?" She said, "Don't you remember? This used to happen to you when you were little. Don't you remember? You used to come home crying."

I didn't remember. I must have told her and then immediately buried my feelings. The only "ching chong" incident that I remembered happened when I was a student at Yale Law School. Walking to a neighborhood market in New Haven one afternoon, I found myself being followed by boys on bikes who were chanting "ching chong," pulling at their eyes, and laughing. I ignored them and kept walking. They followed me for about two blocks and then left. I'm pretty sure that some other people on the street saw what happened, but no one stepped up to say anything. That hurts almost as much as the chants.

Have you ever been taunted by bullies?
How did you react?
Do you wish you had reacted differently?

GRANDMOTHER'S CURE

Early in the morning
when they are still cool
and damp, from dew,
PoPo walks out to the edge
of her vegetable patch
and cuts banana leaves
for my bed.
Large green banana leaves
fresh from her garden
to soothe my red hot
chickenpox itches.

A week before the end of sixth grade, chickenpox broke out at my school. My parents had me skip the last week and drove me to my grandparents' house. It turned out, unfortunately, that we were too late: I had already caught the virus. A few days after I arrived, thousands of itchy red spots broke out all over my body. It was the most severe case of chickenpox that the doctor had ever seen. He said that I needed to be put into quarantine; he recommended that I soak in Calamine baths as much as possible. If I went out, I would infect people. If I scratched, I would have scars. I stayed in the cool bathtub for hours a day.

Early one morning, my grandmother brought a huge green leaf into our bedroom. She told me to lie down on it. This was how her family handled her itching when she was a child with chickenpox in China. It soothed my hot itches instantly.

About five years ago, before our dog Angel came to live with us, I read that pennyroyal is a flea preventive, so I bought some pennyroyal seeds and scattered them in with the grass in the backyard. The pennyroyal has blended in with the grass and you can't really see it. But Angel seems to be able to smell it, and about once a week I spot him burying his nose in the areas where I scattered the seeds. He tosses himself down on the grass, rolling around on his back. Does he know that pennyroyal fights fleas? Does he also know that banana leaves relieve chickenpox itches?

When you're sick, are there special plants
that can help you feel better?
What family remedies do you know about?

DELI CIRCUS

The roast duck clings
by crispy wings
to his Chinese deli trapeze,
slowly swinging back and forth
on an anise-scented breeze.

I love books and movies with talking animals in them, especially when those animals are pigs. I love Wilbur and Olivia and Babe. But I also love bacon. How can I even think about eating Wilbur's cousins? Why am I not a vegetarian?

When I see a Chinese supermarket or restaurant that has a roast duck hanging in the window on a metal meat hook, my imagination immediately transforms the cooked carcass into a live and lovable creature swinging on a circus trapeze. And yet I still eat roast duck. Even just thinking about crispy duck skin sandwiched in pillowy Peking duck buns can make my mouth water.

I admire children who raise farm animals. I think it would be really hard to raise a chicken or pig, to care for it and give it love, knowing that it might end up on a table. Farmers often say the key question is whether an animal was treated humanely. Did it have a good life? Was it able to run around eating all sorts of plants, acorns, fungi, and juicy fresh bugs? If so, then we should not feel bad about eating it.

Duck, did you ever feel like you were flying in a circus?

Do you ever wonder how your food was grown or raised?
If you were in charge of the meals for your family,
what kinds of foods would you buy or grow?

ONE TO TEN

Yut yee sam see
Count in Cantonese with me!

Eun look chut bot
Can you tell me what we've got?

Gow sup. One to ten!
(Could you say that once again?)

Every Lunar New Year, I would go to my Chinese grandparents' apartment and knock on the door. When they came to the door, I would shout out, "Gong hee fat choy, lee cee do loy!"—our Cantonese words for "Happy new year, give me the red envelope!" My grandparents came from Chungsan (also spelled Zhongshan) county in southern China, where Cantonese is spoken. In parts of China where people speak Mandarin or other dialects of Chinese, kids say different words.

My grandmother, my PoPo, would pull a red envelope out of her apron pocket. It was always stuffed with so many bills that it looked very full; but the bills were usually just one-dollar bills—ten of them. If I wanted to keep them, I had to count them out for my grandfather, my GongGong, in Chinese. This is how I learned the numbers in Cantonese. One year I said, "GongGong, I know how to count to a hundred. Do you want to hear?" He did not.

In our family's dialect of Cantonese, we say "lee cee" for "red envelope"; in another part of southern China they might say "lai cee," while in Mandarin a red envelope is called "hongbao." In any kind of Chinese, a red envelope means the same thing: lucky money!

What are your new year traditions?
Are there any holiday customs
that are especially important to your family?

DIM SUM

Steaming
carts roll by full
of identical tins,
each one guarding its own kind of
secret.

Ha gow (shrimp dumplings). Shu mai (shrimp and pork dumplings). Cha shu bao (barbecued pork buns). I could go on and name three dozen different kinds of dim sum and other kinds of Cantonese foods that I love.

I think it's easy for people to learn the words that are most important to them. My Chinese grandparents said many non-food words in Cantonese when I was with them, but the other words didn't stick in my mind. They weren't delicious enough for me to care about them.

Kalbi. Chap chae. Mandoo. The same goes for Korean; I know the names of the foods that I like to eat. In fact, I probably know the names of my favorite foods in a dozen languages.

My favorite thing about school (especially fourth through sixth grade) was our annual international food fair. Parent volunteers would bring food from different cultures; we kids would walk around the auditorium with paper plates, piling on whatever looked good to us. My mother never went to a PTA meeting, but every year she cooked a huge platter for the food fair, either egg foo yung or chow mein noodles or teriyaki chicken. It was the one time of year when she felt useful at my school. Her food always disappeared in minutes. It made me feel proud of my mother—and my school—when I brought the empty platter home.

What are your favorite foods?
Can you write a list of the names of your favorite foods
(in a language other than English)?

JADE

Why do you wear your jade, GongGong?

Look. I tell you.
Old people bone
very crispy.
Break so easy.

Old people fall down
all the time.
Broken bone
be too bad.

Good piece jade
protect you someday.
Fall down,
jade broken. You okay.

How do you know if your jade is good?

Shiny. Green.
Color deep.
Good health in you
make good jade, see?

Sick, jade
look dull. Dead. White.
Your jade young, green.
You all right.

My grandfather was about 85 years old when I first noticed him wearing jewelry—a simple ring carved out of jade, no gold, no decorations. Before then he had never worn any jewelry at all, not even his wedding ring. I asked him why he was wearing it, and he told me why in the words that I used in this poem.

There are many different kinds of jade. His ring was made from the pale green jade that you normally find in jewelry stores, which he called "dull, dead, white." He didn't like that kind of pale jade, so I think he must have bought it because it was affordable. My jade heart, worn as a pendant on a necklace, is made of expensive "apple jade," which is bright green like a Granny Smith apple. It is hard to find this kind of jade now. Beware of fake apple jade, which uses dyes.

My jade heart belonged to my grandmother. She wore it inside her shirt, so you could not see it. She felt that it was a good luck charm that would protect her health. A friend once told me that her jade bracelet, which she started wearing as a child (when her hand could slip through it) and which later fit her snugly (as she grew into an adult), broke in half during rough turbulence on an airplane. She is convinced that her jade bracelet saved the lives of everyone on that flight.

Do you have any good luck charms?
Have you ever been aware
of something extra lucky happening to you?

FUNERAL

They made up
a grandmother
I don't know.
They covered her
eyes with thick
shadow
and painted
loud red
lips on her
quiet mouth.

I put my
handkerchief
near her face.
I told her to use it
when she gets to
that place
to find
her kind
own smile
once again.

My grandmother very rarely wore makeup. When she did, it was just a little lipstick, a soft rosy color, and maybe eyebrow pencil to fill in the bare spots. So I was shocked when, at her funeral, I saw her face made up in bright colors. In the open casket, she did not look like herself. I imagined her soul floating above her body, her forehead wrinkled in confusion and her mouth in a tight frown. I wish they had kept the casket closed.

It must be really hard to work with the bodies at a mortuary. I cannot imagine doing such a job. We're lucky that there are people who are willing to do it. They have no idea of what the people, when they were alive, were like. Were they funny? Were they kind? Did they wear a lot of makeup or none at all? We can give them photos, but do you look "like yourself" in every photo? In some photos I look bored, or angry, or confused. I wouldn't want the mortuary to have those photos of me.

I don't look or act like my best self when I'm sick with the flu, or when I've had too little sleep, or even when I'm just stressed out from having too much to do. Maybe we all should take a picture of our best selves, when we're feeling happy and relaxed, and keep these pictures in our pockets at all times with a note that says, "THIS is the REAL me!"

What does the REAL you look like?
What would you be doing and where would you be
in photos of "your best self"?

STROKE

When Mother said "stroke"
my head went swimming.
I thought of summer
at the city pool.
I never thought of you,
Grandpa,
lying in bed,
unable to move,
trying to say, "I love you, too,"
through your watery eyes.

My eyes water all the time. A lot. People sometimes think I'm crying when I'm just reacting to pollen. When I was a child, my doctor made me rinse my eyes four times a day with a special eye wash that came in a blue bottle. During hay fever season, other kids ran out to the field, and I ran to the bathroom to rinse my eyes. I'm an expert on watery eyes.

When I saw Pop (my father-in-law) in the nursing home, propped up in his bed, unable to speak due to his stroke, unable to move his arms due to his worsening ALS (Lou Gehrig's disease), I saw the water in his eyes and I knew it wasn't hay fever.

In this poem I wrote "Mother" instead of "my mother-in-law." I wrote "Grandpa" instead of "Pop." I didn't think immediately of the city pool when I heard about Pop's stroke, but it's true that my head was "swimming"; I didn't feel like my normal self. Sometimes I take a bunch of real-life experiences and mash them together with new facts in my writing. You can do that, too. You can invent names. You can change facts. But even if you write a fantasy novel with invented characters, make sure to put some true feelings in. Think about your strongest memories—happy times, sad times, frustrated feelings—and get some real details down on paper. It's all right if your eyes water a little bit while you're remembering these things. Blame it on hay fever and keep on writing.

Can you think of something right now
that might make you cry?
Can you write about it—just for yourself?

BELATED BIRTHDAY

Dust wraps the present
I meant to give to my friend
as snow hides his grave.

One of my friends used to give me random little gifts for no reason. My favorite gifts from her were homegrown Meyer lemons that she picked herself from her garden. How many people give lemons to their friends? I liked that they were an unusual gift. This friend of mine, Elaine, is an unusual person. She is an artist who once made a piece of art out of sausage skins.

I keep a special "gift closet" full of little gifts, mostly things that cost less than five dollars. Right now in my gift closet I have a bar of soap, some bookmarks, and a fancy fly swatter. One item that I had in the gift closet for a few years was a book that I had wrapped for my friend Tony. I thought about sending it to him as a gift for no reason, but then I decided to save it for his birthday.

A couple of months before his birthday, though, Tony died. He was only 33 years old. After I learned of his death, I didn't know what to do with the present. I kept the book in the gift closet until we moved, and then I put it in a box for Goodwill. After I donated it, I remembered that I had put a very short note inside the book. If you are ever shopping at a Goodwill store and you find a book with a note that says, "Happy birthday, Tony"—now you know the story.

Have you ever surprised someone with a gift?
What's a favorite gift that you've received
that was handmade or homegrown?

REMEMBERING WHEN

She sits cross-legged
in the ripped den chair,
slouched, slumping,
staring somewhere—
holding her glass
with both hands.

Mom drinks a lot.
Too much, I guess.
She's getting worse.
She looks a mess.
She used to be pretty,
I tell my friends.

I carry a picture
remembering when.

It's hard to know when something moves from a "favorite thing" to a "problem."

I like eating potato chips. Do I have a potato chips problem?

I like poetry books. Do I have a poetry problem?

At one point in her life, my mother liked sitting in her chair in the family room for hours, drinking beer. The TV would be on, but she wouldn't be watching it. After a while, I understood that this was not just a favorite thing of hers, but a problem. Then one day, on her own, she stopped drinking. The problem went away. Sometimes problems go away on their own. And sometimes they don't. People don't expect kids to help, but you're right there. You're seeing it. You're living with it. So, yes, you can ask for help. You can give help, too.

When my mother was very sad, or very tired, I would try really hard to do a little extra work around the house. I would fold the laundry and cook the rice (easy to do with our electric rice cooker). I would straighten up the dining room. When I'm feeling a lot of stress nowadays, sometimes I take five minutes to straighten up my house.

And sometimes I just eat potato chips.

Is there anything that you can do
to make yourself feel calm?
Is there anything you can do to help your family?

Home

This house
of ours, with its
chipped paint, torn screens and leaks,
is still the best place I have known—
my home.

We moved a lot when I was growing up. Usually we lived in apartments, but from third grade through sixth grade we lived in a house in San Anselmo, California. It was high on a hill, one of the tallest hills in town. I loved our view at night: the world below us looked like black velvet filled with little golden dots of light.

The house was plain, which is why we could afford it. Some of our neighbors' houses were big and fancy. Actually, our house wasn't just plain; it needed a lot of work when we bought it. Some of the screens on the windows and sliding doors were torn where fingers had pushed through them, and paint peeled off the wooden posts outside. Even with all these little defects, I loved our house. We spent weekends fixing it up. We painted. We planted fruit trees. My father and I even built a redwood fence together so we could have a dog in our backyard.

We lived there for less than four years, but it felt like much longer. I can still remember the feel of the carpet, the smell of the fireplace, the shape of the kitchen, and the tile in the bathrooms. The new owners of the house might change it, but that house will always be the same in my mind.

Have you lived in more than one place?
What are (or were) the best things
about your favorite home?

CHOPSTICKS AND TEA

They use chopsticks.
They drink tea.
Why is it fork and
water for me?

I'll take chopsticks.
Tea, too, please.
Why does it matter
that I'm not Chinese?

I didn't learn how to use chopsticks properly until I was 10 or 11 years old. Before then, I mainly used the "stab your food" method and I would lean close to my plate or bowl so the food wouldn't have time to fall. Even after I learned to use chopsticks correctly (in my mind), my mother told me that I was still holding them wrong. The problem is that I am not very coordinated. Other people can braid their hair without any effort, but my braids look messy and fall apart. When you pair my hand coordination with my poor vision, watch out! One day I almost skewered multiple people in a game of darts.

My husband Glenn, who first used chopsticks when he was in college, uses them expertly because he is very coordinated. He can pick up a slippery piece of tofu or even a small grain of rice. So it's funny when Chinese waiters bring me chopsticks, but give Glenn a fork. When they bring one glass of water and give it to him, and one cup of tea for me, we trade. I'm sure that they do this because of his light pink French-German face.

The first time that Glenn went to my grandfather's house for dinner, my grandfather cooked some very authentic Chinese foods. We had greens with fermented tofu, bitter melon with fermented black beans, and fermented fish. Fermented foods are good for you, but also very smelly. Each place was set with chopsticks; no forks. This was a test in more than one way—and Glenn got an A+!

Do people sometimes underestimate you?
Can you think of good ways
to surprise them?

OX AND SNAKE

I was born
in the year of the ox
it says on the back
of this cracker box.

What about you?
I bet you're a snake,
the way you swallowed
that whole moon cake!

Every once in a while I'll ask someone what their Asian zodiac animal is and when they tell me, I'll think, "Exactly! Of course! You couldn't be anything else." Someone who likes to collect trinkets and is very clever is a natural Rat. Someone who likes to run free and travel is a natural Horse.

Some of the zodiac animals are different in different Asian cultures; for instance, 2023 is the Chinese year of the rabbit, but it is the Vietnamese year of the cat. What would you rather be: Rabbit or Cat?

At an Asian market, you can find boxes of cookies or crackers with pictures of the Chinese zodiac animals and a list of their years. You can also do a quick online search to find your animal year. I was born in the year of the tiger. Tiger people (1962, 1974, 1986, 1998, 2010, 2022) are supposed to be decisive and energetic. I think I am a decisive and energetic person. Is this because I'm a Tiger? I know some people who were born in the year of the tiger but they seem to be much more like Dogs—easygoing, friendly, and relaxed. If you tell people born in the year of the ox that Ox people are hard-working and determined, they will probably start working harder. Maybe astrology isn't really a true guide to who we are—but can help us decide who we want to be?

What is your Chinese zodiac animal?
Are you like that animal in some ways?
Are you unlike that animal in other ways?

Over My Head

GongGong talks in Chinese
over my head.
I don't understand
a word that's said,
but the way the shopkeeper's
nodding my way
makes me think this will be
a very good day.

As I've said before, I don't speak much Chinese or Korean except for favorite foods, but I usually can tell if someone is talking about me in a foreign language. Part of it is the way they smile (or frown) at you while talking. Or sometimes you hear a few familiar words slipped into the sentence and you can guess the rest. My dog only needs to hear me say, "blah blah blah walk blah blah blah park" to get excited. He doesn't need to know all the words.

Generally, it's not part of traditional Asian culture to give compliments directly to kids at home because children are supposed to be modest and humble. If you tell your kids how great they are, then they might not work as hard. But parents and grandparents are allowed to boast, and boasting in public to friends and shopkeepers—especially if your kids cannot understand you—is something that Asian parents and grandparents do all the time.

Just bow your head and stare at the floor, and they will be doubly proud.

Think about the compliments
that you would give to yourself, if you were someone else—
and go on, give them to yourself right now!

After the Parade

Bits of red paper
swirl on the ground
like firecracker ghosts
prowling around,
searching for souls
lost with the year,
trying to calm
their dragon fear
before they fly
away together,
to live in the world
of dragons forever.

What do writers do? We look around. A lot. We look closely. We notice things like bits of red paper on the ground and we invent stories in our mind to explain what those bits of paper are all about. We listen carefully not just to what people say, but how they say it, what words, what tone. We listen for the unspoken words, too.

When I was a child, I wrote only when I had schoolwork or homework, never for fun. I tried to do a good job so that I could earn stars and honors and A grades to please my parents. But I never imagined myself working as a writer.

My mother could barely write in English. In Korean, she wrote only as well as a fourth grader, because five years of school was all that her family could afford to pay. The only school in her town was a Catholic school that charged tuition —and, besides, they needed her to work. But she had a poet's eye. If I changed one tiny thing about my appearance, no matter how small, she would notice. She had a poet's voice, too. One day, instead of saying that she thought my father's dreams were unrealistic, she said: "He is trying to grab the wind."

Not everything that a poet notices or says needs to be beautiful. But sometimes we'll look at litter and think of dragons.

Who is the most "writerly" person you know?
What are some of the things that they notice?
What are some of the things that they say?

At a Chinese Feast

Black grass jello?
Sweet bean soup?
Tapioca?
What's that goop?
MmmMango pudding—
isn't bad.
You know something?
I'm half glad
they didn't have
my ice-cream pie.
Could I give
that soup a try?

There are many trade names that we use as generic nouns and verbs. For example, we might do an online search; but more often we just "google" something. We might reach for a tissue; but more often we just blow our noses in "kleenex."

When this poem was published originally, the first line read "black grass gelatin" because the copyeditor insisted on it. She said that we couldn't use "black jello," as I'd written, because "Jell-O" was a registered trademark. This really bothered me because I had never used the word "gelatin" in my whole life, even though I knew what it was. I could've used the words "grass jelly," since that is what it says on the can that you buy at the Asian market, but we never called it "grass jelly" at home. It was always "black jello." And I like my poems to sound like the way I talk.

Whenever I eat black jello, I instantly relax. I love the slightly bittersweet flavor. I love the way it's soft and jiggly and served very cold. Black jello is one of my "comfort foods." I take one bite and I am suddenly 10 years old again with a bowl in one hand and a spoon in the other, sitting on the couch, singing along to The Partridge Family: "Come on, get happy!"

What are your favorite "comfort foods"?
Why do you love them so much?

NOODLES

Noodles for breakfast,
noodles for lunch,
noodles for dinner,
noodles that crunch,
noodles to twirl,
noodles to slurp—
I could eat noodles
all day! Burp!

I remember a Sunday in fifth grade when I got to invite a friend over for brunch. I felt so happy when I heard my mother chopping pork. *Bam! Bam! Bam!* She never bought ground pork, but instead chopped up a big chunk of pork with her cleaver, sitting on the floor on a towel, with a thick cutting board in front of her. Pork and shrimp, chopped together into a smooth mix, meant we would be having wonton noodle soup. This was my favorite food for any meal, breakfast, lunch, or dinner.

My friend came late. The table was set with the bowls of steaming wonton noodle soup. She took one quick look, wrinkled her nose, and said, "Noodle soup for breakfast? Don't you eat normal food?" Yes, sometimes we did eat "normal" food—bacon and eggs, potatoes, or pancakes—but when we were lucky we had wonton noodle soup. She hurt my feelings. I should've said something to her, but I didn't. I think my mother's feelings were hurt, too, but she never talked about things like that.

Years later, I wrote a list of childhood memories that stood out. This memory bubbled up. It made me angry, so I wrote an angry poem. But then I stepped back for a minute and realized that the poem didn't need to be angry. I just needed to say, "It's OK to eat noodles for breakfast." But I love noodles for lunch, too, and we eat pasta at least once a week for dinner. I guess I could shorten this poem to five words: "Eat noodles / whenever / you want!"

Have you ever been angry at someone—
or just sad or disappointed—and kept those feelings inside?
Can you write about it now?

DINNER

Crowded in cages, chickens cluck:
"Wouldn't you rather eat roast duck?"

Catfish swimming in the fish tank sing:
"Lobster meat is the tastiest thing!"

When we come to pick our dinner,
no one wants to be the winner.

When I hear birds chirping and cheeping, I often wonder what they're saying. Sometimes it sounds like they're saying, "What a beautiful morning! The sun feels warm and the berries are sweet!" And sometimes it sounds like they're saying, "Go away! Yes, you! You're making me nervous! Scram!"

I'm guessing that all robins understand robins. I'm guessing that all chickens understand chickens, too. But do chickens understand robins? Do chickens understand ducks?

There is a Chinese saying that is sometimes used to describe two people who can't understand each other: "like a chicken talking to a duck." I disagree with that idea. I can communicate with my dog. Why can't chickens talk to ducks?

A chicken might not fully understand when a duck says something that it's never experienced, such as "the lake was so clear, you could see a hundred fish swimming." And a duck might not understand when a chicken says, "we felt so safe, shut in our cozy little coop." But I'll bet chickens understand when ducks say, "A storm is coming." And I'm guessing everyone on a farm understands when the farmer pulls up with a truck full of cages and says, "How about a little trip to the market?"

Have you ever felt "like a chicken talking to a duck"?
Are there topics where we seem unable to understand each other,
even if we're hearing the same words?

CHINESE VALENTINE

They say
it is bad luck
to cut a long green bean.
I give you this bean, like my love—
whole, fresh.

One afternoon my grandfather was preparing dinner, washing some foot-long Chinese green beans, when he said, "Long beans give long life. Cut beans, cut life short." I decided to write about that memory. When my poem was published, I read it aloud to my grandfather and he laughed. "If you no cut," he said, "how can you eat it? Long bean is not soft like spaghetti!"

I was sure he had told me that we should not cut long beans. But then I thought back to all the meals he'd prepared with long beans—and yes, the beans that I'd eaten had always been cut. Did he leave them long and whole just for that one dinner? I'm sure he did. But maybe he was just playing with me. He liked to joke around; once we were in a restaurant and he ate a lobster, then reassembled the empty shell to fool the waiter into thinking that he'd been given a "ghost lobster."

I was really upset about the long beans because the poem had been published with this (wrong) bit of wisdom about not cutting the beans. But then I remembered what my teacher Myra Cohn Livingston had said about a cinquain (a five-line poem with a 2-4-6-8-2 syllable count, like "Chinese Valentine"). She said a cinquain should have a very important first line. The first line in this poem is "They say"; and yes, *they* are constantly saying things that might not be true. It's up to us to listen and think—and read and read and read!

What kinds of things have you heard lately
that don't make sense?
How can you find information you can trust?

STRANGERS

Sometimes strangers talk so fast,
so rough,
so big—
you wonder if it's just a bluff.

They can make you feel so weak,
so small,
so dumb—
you wonder if they know it all.

But maybe they're the ones who need
someone to follow. Take the lead.

My mother used to get angry at me when I went to a store in old clothes. She felt that we needed to look extra sharp when we were around strangers because there weren't many Asians in our neighborhood, and people would be quick to judge us. And sometimes she was right. I wrote this poem remembering a visit to a carpet store where the salesman treated us poorly. He acted like we had no right even to look at such expensive carpet. It was indeed too expensive for us, but I was angry at the way he treated us.

His snobby behavior made me decide that I didn't like the carpet, anyway. This wasn't true: it was beautiful carpet, extremely soft and full, with deep rich colors. I let him spoil my feelings about that carpet. In a way, I let him spoil my feelings about myself that day, too. This felt like discrimination to me. It felt like racism, even though there was nothing that he said about my race. And it hurt. When small instances of discrimination—what we might call "microaggressions"—happen all the time, they build up. This is how we become powerless.

The next time something happens that makes you feel bad, talk to someone about it. The next time you see someone being made to feel small, try to speak up. When a bunch of good things happen, even small things, they all add up—and this is how we become powerful.

Has anyone ever made you "feel small" in a bad way?
Have you ever seen anyone putting someone down?
What could you do next time?

DAD

Watch out.
Mad, he snaps
like a turtle.
His face blows up
round.
His mouth thins
to a frown.
He sticks his neck out
in a dare.
Beware.
Quick as he strikes,
he draws back,
hiding in his tough
hard shell.

I love my father very much. He is smart and funny. But I hate it when he gets mad. Everybody gets mad, right? When reasonable people are upset, they talk things over. They work things out. At least they try.

Not my father. When he gets mad, he does not want to talk about it. You can tell he's angry, but sometimes you don't even know why. If you don't know why someone is mad, how can you make things better?

When I was writing the original version of this book, my father came to visit me for the weekend. Things were going great, until something made him mad. I was determined not to let it bother me. I thought, "If he wants to be mad, let him be mad. I'm going to go and write a poem about him." I sat at the kitchen table and let the words flow. Many drafts later, it became this poem.

When someone makes you mad, or sad, or confused, that's a good time to write a poem. But if you write something that could possibly make someone upset, maybe you should change the names and facts. Or tear it up into a hundred little bits, so you won't get in trouble!

When you get mad, are you willing to talk about it?
What's the best way for someone to talk to you
when you are upset?

ORPHAN

Tell this foster family
no one ever keeps me long.
I've been passed around this town
like a beat-up hand-me-down.
Tell them must be something wrong.
Can't be—can it?—they *want* me.

This poem is about a friend of mine. He was so kind and always seemed so happy, I never would have known that he had been through difficult times. If it had been me, I think I would be bitter about the bad things that had happened in my life.

I had known him already for about eight months before he told me that he had been orphaned and in and out of foster homes. I don't know what made him decide to share this with me. I wonder if he asked himself, "When is the right time to tell her about my childhood?" Or if the memories just popped into his mind at that moment, and so he told me his story.

When I first heard the details, I felt very, very sad for him. But then I felt happy. I was so relieved that he eventually found a mother who loved him very much. Thinking about it now, he actually might be the "most loved child" of anyone I know. There is someone out there for each of us—maybe even a whole bunch of someones. Maybe that's what life is all about: finding those people, one by one.

If you could choose a new family,
who would you choose?
Who would you like to choose you?

Immigrant Boy

He and I are not the same,
though we look alike to you.
He was born here. I am new.
Just three months ago I came.

I followed him around today.
He does not like me to be near.
I wonder—had I been born here,
would he then want me to play?

When I was in college at UCLA, I took French classes every year. I even lived in France for one year, my junior year. When I was a senior, a new student joined our Advanced French class a few weeks late. Everyone was already seated when she walked into the classroom. Our teacher looked around, pointed to me, and told her, "Sit near Janet. She will help you."

The girl had grown up in Vietnam and had attended a French school there as a child. She knew more French than any of us. I wondered why I had been picked to help her. It's possible that I was chosen because I was very good at French. But looking around, suddenly I became aware that I was the only Asian in the class—except for this girl. It seemed to me that I had been chosen to help her simply because I was Asian. But I was nothing like this girl. She was wearing frilly clothes; I was dressed in simple clothes. She had long, curled hair and lots of make-up; I had short hair and a plain face. It made me mad that we had been lumped together. So I gave her no help at all. I can still remember how sad she looked after she saw that I did not want to be her friend.

When I wrote this poem, I remembered how poorly I had treated her and I felt guilty. I decided to reverse the identities, and to write this poem while imagining myself as an immigrant child.

Have you ever been very unfriendly to someone—
even though they did nothing wrong?
How do you think they felt?

To Caged Birds at the Poultry Store

I've seen those bullies step on you.
It makes you want to scratch and kick.
I wonder why they do it, too.

Let them climb to the top of the pile,
even though it makes you sick.
Trust me, trust me; wait awhile.

Though waiting at the bottom's tough,
just when you have had enough
you'll see the butcher's hands reach in—
and trust me, you're the ones who win.

My grandfather and I often went shopping in Chinatown together. He never liked to go to the big supermarkets there. Instead, we would visit half a dozen little shops, buying vegetables at the small produce store, fish at the small seafood store that had live fish and crabs and lobsters swimming in tanks, and freshly-killed chicken at the poultry store.

The cages were piled high outside the poultry store. While I waited for my grandfather, I would watch the chickens squirming around in the cages. I felt sorry for the runty ones who were stepped on by stronger chickens wanting to get a better spot in the top and front areas of the cages. But when the butcher's hands reached in—well, the poem says it all.

Have you ever felt bullied or just unlucky,
like a chicken stuck at the bottom of the cage?
Have you ever thought, "Phew! That was a lucky break!"

SOME
ADDITIONAL
THOUGHTS

WRITING ABOUT RACISM

The first poems of mine that received any praise from my poetry teacher Myra Cohn Livingston were "Waiting at the Railroad Café" and "Noise." She wanted me to write more poems like those, poems that came from a very personal place deep inside me. Before then, in the hundreds of poems that I wrote for homework, I was mainly trying to be clever about made-up things, things that had no connection with my real life.

When I started writing about racism, it felt like such a relief. It's hard to write about painful memories—but we all have them. We all have experiences where someone has hurt us. We all have times when we've hurt someone else and felt bad about it later. One way to make it easier to write about hard things is to promise yourself to rip it up. Write for five minutes and then—even if you actually love what you wrote—tear it up into a hundred little pieces and throw it away. Do this every night for a week and you will, guaranteed, become a better writer. And a happier person, too. Sometimes just writing words down is enough; you don't need anyone to read them.

I decided to write an "& MORE" version of this book because, ever since the start of the pandemic in early 2020, we've seen a lot of hate twisted into racist acts against Asians. Americans who are obsessed with the Chinese origins of the coronavirus are blaming Asians in America for COVID—even Asian Americans who have never been to Asia. These people believe that Asians will never belong in America, that we are foreign and should "go back" to where we came from.

In many of these attacks, witnesses were there. These witnesses weren't racist themselves, but they often stood by doing nothing, allowing the racist attacks to continue. Many of them said later that they wished they'd stepped up and shouted for help. It can be hard to know what to do if you find yourself in the middle of trouble, which makes it extra important to think and talk in advance about what you would do. Around the country, adults who are trying to become antiracist are taking "bystander training." They are learning how to distract attackers and document what's happening.

Kids can do this too; ask about it.

As I pointed out in my poems "Speak Up," "Noise," "Waiting at the Railroad Café," and "Bombs Bursting in Air," anti-Asian racism is often subtle. It's someone badgering you into speaking a few words of an Asian language. It's someone pulling at their eyes while laughing. It's everyone ignoring you, as if you were invisible. It's people acting like you couldn't possibly fit in at a baseball game. In "Strangers," it's a mean man judging you at the store because of the way you look. A bully trying to make you feel unimportant and small.

These "microaggressions" might not seem to be seriously harmful, but when you have to deal with them all the time—especially when you have to deal with them alone—they can drag you down.

If you are facing racism, write about it. If you are witnessing racism, write about it. Keep those pieces of writing in your desk drawer and read them every week to give you courage. Or, if you feel comfortable, you can share your work. Make your voice heard among people who need to know, and follow up to see that changes are made.

Every landmark civil rights case started with words. People talking. Lawyers writing. Judges reading. Jurors listening. Bystanders asking the right questions. Think about the last time you felt inspired and important. It was because of words, right? Maybe you heard a superhero make a speech about the goodness in people. Maybe you listened to Amanda Gorman's poem at the 2021 presidential inauguration. Words can lift us up.

WHY NOT YOU?

When I quit my law job because I wanted to write children's books, I imagined that I would write picture books. I never thought I would write poetry. I hated poetry, starting about fourth grade. Or at least I thought I hated it. What I hated, actually, was poetry homework. I hated picking poems apart, trying to find the "true" meaning in them. I hated needing to memorize a poem. I hated standing in front of everyone, mind blank, having forgotten it.

When I heard Myra Cohn Livingston read her poems at a one-day workshop at UCLA, I knew I could learn something from her. I didn't want to learn how to write poems, though; I just wanted to learn how to use poetic techniques like rhyme to make my "regular writing" sound better. She told me that I needed to read more poetry, just one book after the other, very quickly. So I started reading a backpack full of poetry books each week—and I fell in love with poems.

Even if you have no intention of being a full-time poet, writing poems will make you a happier person. All your complicated feelings—your anger, your sadness, your silliness, your confusion, your jealousy, your joy—will have a place to go: in poems.

Poetry is especially useful when you're feeling bored. Writing poetry feels like playing with words. Try writing a list poem of a bunch of random (or not-random) words. List the foods that you ate yesterday, or things that you heard on TV, or some of the song lyrics that are stuck in your head. Look around the room and add words that describe what you see: onion, scissors, pillow, shoes. Next thing you know, you'll have the start of a poem—or at least a wonderful "word bank." It's that easy. Your head will feel lighter; your mind will feel awake.

Writing a poem is the easiest kind of writing. With poems, anything goes. If you want to write with no punctuation, no capital letters, made-up and mashed-up words and words used in strange ways that seem to make no sense—well, you might become as famous as E.E. Cummings. Why not you?

ABOUT THE AUTHOR

Janet Wong is a graduate of Yale Law School and a former lawyer who switched careers to become a children's author. Her dramatic career change has been featured on *The Oprah Winfrey Show*, CNN's *Paula Zahn Show*, and *Radical Sabbatical*. She is the author of more than 35 books for children and teens on a wide variety of subjects, including identity (*A Suitcase of Seaweed & MORE*), writing and revision (*You Have to Write*), diversity and community (*Apple Pie 4th of July*), peer pressure (*Me and Rolly Maloo*), driving (*Behind the Wheel: Poems about Driving*), chess (*Alex and the Wednesday Chess Club*), and yoga (*Twist: Yoga Poems*). A frequent featured speaker at literacy conferences, Wong has served as a member of several national committees, including the NCTE Poetry Committee and the ILA Notable Books for a Global Society committee.

She is the 2021 winner of the NCTE Excellence in Poetry for Children award, a lifetime achievement award that is one of the highest honors a children's poet can receive. You can find more info about Janet Wong at **JanetWong.com**. Read about her work with Sylvia Vardell at **PomeloBooks.com**.

QUILT

Our family
is a quilt

of odd remnants
patched together

in a strange
pattern,

threads fraying,
fabric wearing thin—

but made to keep
its warmth

even in bitter
cold.

PoPo:
The blue twill of my Winnie-the-Pooh jacket.

GongGong:
The canvas he learned to paint on when he was 88.

My Korean grandparents, Halmoni and Haraboji:
Stiff beige linen, the clothes of old-time farmers.

My father:
Wide-wale corduroy.
A life of ups and downs.

My mother:
An ivory-colored vinyl tablecloth, embossed with flowers.
A cigarette burn in it.

Me:
Boiled wool.

All of us, now and then:
Rough patches.

Swatches of smooth silk:
we can hope.

What kind of fabrics
might you choose for your family?
For you?

Made in the USA
Las Vegas, NV
13 October 2021